TAKE US TO YOUR MALL

Other FoxTrot Books by Bill Amend

FoxTrot
Pass the Loot
Black Bart Says Draw
Eight Yards, Down and Out
Bury My Heart at Fun-Fun Mountain
Say Hello to Cactus Flats
May the Force Be With Us, Please

Anthologies

FoxTrot: The Works
FoxTrot *en masse*
Enormously FoxTrot

FoxTrot is distributed internationally by Universal Press Syndicate.

ISBN 0-590-74354-6

12 11 10 9 8 7 6 5 4 3 2 1   6 7 8 9/9 0 1/0

Printed in the U.S.A.   34

First Scholastic printing, February 1996

TAKE US TO YOUR MALL

A FoxTrot Collection
by Bill Amend

SCHOLASTIC INC.

New York Toronto London Auckland Sydney

To Madeline

THINK FAST, PAIGE!

HUH?

SPLOOSH!

AMEND

RUN FAST, JASON.

THINK FAST, JASON...

PETER!

GLUG GLUG GLUG

AMEND

HOW MANY TIMES DO I HAVE TO TELL YOU NOT TO DRINK OUT OF THE MILK CARTON?!

IT'S DISGUSTING, IT'S UNSANITARY AND IT'S INCONSIDERATE TO THE REST OF US WHO HAVE TO DRINK IT AFTER YOU!

THAT IS, IF WE EVER COULD DRINK IT AFTER YOU.

MIND IF I MAKE A SANDWICH BEFORE DINNER?

KNOCK-KNOCK.

WHO'S THERE?

QUINCY.

QUINCY-WHO?

QUINCY THE FLYING IGUANA!

AIEEE!

AMEND

THAT ONE MAY NEED RETOOLING...

I THOUGHT THE ENDING WAS FUNNY.

NO DEEP-SPACE METEORS CRASHING DOWN ON OUR HEADS...

NO RADIOACTIVE SPIDERS INFECTING OUR BLOOD-STREAMS...

NO BLASTS OF COSMIC ENERGY MUTATING OUR CELLS...

AT THIS RATE WE'RE **NEVER** GONNA BE SUPERHEROES.

O YE OF LITTLE FAITH...

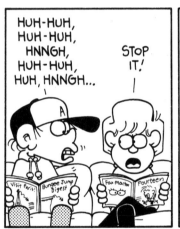

HUH-HUH, HUH-HUH, HNNGH, HUH-HUH, HUH, HNNGH...

STOP IT!

HUH-HUH, HNNGH, HUH-HUH, HUH-HUH, HNNGH...

I SAID, **CUT IT OUT!**

HUH-HUH, HNNGH...

MOM, PETER'S DOING THAT STUPID "BEAVIS AND BUTT-HEAD" LAUGH AND HE'S DRIVING ME NUTS!

PETER, GO DO YOUR HOMEWORK.

THANK YOU, MISS TATTLETALE.

HUH-HUH, HUH-HUH, HNNGH, HUH-HUH, HNNGH...

YOU TOO, PAIGE.

PAIGE HAS BEEN TAKING VITAMINS WITH IRON.

OH, MAN, IF THIS WORKS...

FoxTrot
BILL AMEND

VERY FUNNY, PAIGE, BUT I'M STILL NOT RAISING THE THERMOSTAT.

WHATEVER YOU SAY, NANOOK.

AMEND

MOTHER, I WANT A CAT.

A CAT.

A KITTY CAT. YOU KNOW, THE KIND WITH BIG, GREEN EYES, THOSE ITTY-BITTY PAWS, CUTE LITTLE EARS AND LOTS AND LOTS OF POOFY FUR...

PLEEEASE?

PETER AND JASON ARE ALLERGIC TO CATS.

WHY DO YOU THINK I **WANT** ONE?

PAIGE, NO. AND ABOUT THESE ATTACK DOG BROCHURES...

GREETINGS... YOUNG... STRANGER...

I AM... KWAI CHANG JASON... SHAOLIN PRIEST-IN-... TRAINING...

I SEARCH... FOR THE ANSWER... TO THE QUESTION... IF THE TIGER... EATS THE LOTUS... BLOSSOM... IS HIS BREATH... AS BAD... AS... YOURS?...

THIS IS WHY SHAOLIN PRIESTS KNOW KUNG FU.

YOU LEFT YOUR CARDBOARD NINJA STARS.

UM, WE'RE OUT OF CHOCO HONEY CRUNCH AGAIN.

I THINK WE'VE ACTUALLY REACHED A POINT WHERE LOX AND BAGELS WOULD BE CHEAPER.

BUT THE SPECTACLE, MOTHER... THE **SPECTACLE**...

WOULD I STILL GET DECODER RINGS?

WE'RE OUT OF CHOCO HONEY CRUNCH?!

PERFECT.

I'LL ONLY ASK YOU ONCE. WHERE'S MY HOMEWORK?

OK! OK! I HID IT IN MY CLOSET!...

MOM, YOU'D BETTER LET ME MAKE MY OWN SANDWICH TODAY.

WHY'S THAT?

YOU KNOW HOW WHEN I HAVE A MATH TEST SCHEDULED I LIKE IT CUT INTO TRAPEZOIDS FOR GOOD LUCK AND WHEN I HAVE A VOCABULARY QUIZ I LIKE IT CUT INTO OVALS?

YESSS...

WELL, TODAY I HAVE BOTH.

I SEE.

I JUST WISH I KNEW WHAT A TRAPOVALOID LOOKED LIKE.

THERE'S A PROTRACTOR IN THE BREAD DRAWER.

MAYBE THERE'S JUST NO SUCH THING AS A FRISBEE IGUANA.

ONE MORE TRY...

ARE THESE PAIGE'S CDs?

Wanted Preferably Dead

9

FoxTrot
BILL AMEND

MOM, CAN I HAVE SOME MONEY?

WHAT FOR?

MY CLASS IS HAVING A HALLOWEEN COSTUME CONTEST ON FRIDAY AND I REALLY, REALLY, **REALLY** WANT TO WIN.

TEN DOLLARS OUGHT TO BE ENOUGH.

TO BUY A COSTUME?

TO BUY THE JUDGE.

AS MUCH AS I'D LIKE TO BE A PARTY TO YOUR VICTORY...

PAIGE, I NEED YOUR ADVICE FOR THIS HALLOWEEN COSTUME CONTEST THEY'RE HAVING AT SCHOOL.

WHAT SORT OF ADVICE?

I THINK I WANT TO GO AS A ROTTING, MANGLED ZOMBIE CORPSE, BUT I DON'T KNOW MUCH ABOUT ROTTING ZOMBIE MAKEUP.

WHAT KIND DO **YOU** USE?

FOR HALLOWEEN?

I MEAN, THE STUFF YOU HAVE ON NOW.

YOU KNOW, IF YOU'D **REALLY** LIKE TO LOOK LIKE A MANGLED CORPSE...

JASON, PLEASE— I HAVE TO GO START DINNER.

THIS'LL ONLY TAKE A SECOND.

WHICH DO YOU THINK WORKS BETTER FOR HALLOWEEN— HAVING THESE FAKE INTESTINES SPILLING OUT OF MY STOMACH...

OR DANGLING OUT OF MY MOUTH?

I GUESS DINNER CAN WAIT.

IN THAT CASE, LET ME ALSO ASK YOU ABOUT THESE GLUE-ON BOILS...

AM I THE PERFECT ZOMBIE, OR WHAT?

YOU'RE ADORABLE. NOW GO DO YOUR HOMEWORK.

ADORABLE?! I'M A ZOMBIE, MOTHER! I'M SUPPOSED TO BE GRUESOME!

YOU'RE RIGHT. YOU'RE GRUESOME. NOW, GO.

YOU'RE JUST SAYING THAT! YOU THINK I'M ADORABLE! AAAAAA!

YOU KNOW, I'M NOT SURE ZOMBIES ARE SUPPOSED TO BE QUITE SO HIGH-STRUNG.

I KNEW I SHOULD'VE SPRUNG FOR THOSE ZOMBIE TEETH DELUXE...

5th GRADE HALLOWEEN COSTUME CONTEST

Grrr Grrr Grrr Grrr Grrr Grrr Grrr Grrr

UM, PERHAPS PRINCIPAL MARTINI WOULD LIKE TO ANNOUNCE THE WINNERS?...

OH NO, THESE ARE YOUR MONSTERS, MISS O'MALLEY.

SO HOW WAS THE COSTUME CONTEST?

PRETTY GOOD. I WON "MOST REALISTIC."

JASON, CONGRATULATIONS! THAT'S GREAT!

IT'S OK. WHAT I REALLY WANTED TO WIN WAS "BEST OF SHOW," BUT I WAS DISQUALIFIED BEFORE THE FINAL JUDGING.

WHAT FOR?

TRYING TO EAT THE VISIBLE MAN'S INNARDS.

YOU KNOW, THE GOOD METHOD ACTORS SET LIMITS.

ANYWAY, YOU MAY GET A PHONE CALL...

FoxTrot
BILL AMEND

"MARY LOU WANTS TO PLANT A FLOWER GARDEN."

"IF HER PLOT IS 8'x10' AND THE SEEDS MUST BE SPACED AT LEAST ONE FOOT APART, WHAT IS THE LARGEST NUMBER OF SEEDS SHE CAN PLANT?"

WELL?

ZERO. IT'S NOVEMBER.

DID I MENTION HOW EXCITED I AM THAT YOU'RE PAYING ME BY THE HOUR?

I SUPPOSE SHE COULD BE LIVING IN AUSTRALIA...

I HATE WORD PROBLEMS.

ARE YOU KIDDING? WORD PROBLEMS ARE GREAT!

WITHOUT WORD PROBLEMS, MATH WOULD BE JUST SOME ABSTRACT BUNCH OF FORMULAS THAT LIVE ONLY WITHIN THE CONFINES OF A CLASSROOM OR A TEXTBOOK.

BUT IN REALITY, MATH IS EVERYWHERE YOU LOOK! IT PERMEATES EVERYTHING! YOU CAN'T ESCAPE IT! AND THAT'S WHAT WORD PROBLEMS LET US IN ON.

AND THAT'S **NOT** A REASON TO HATE THEM?

AND THE MORE MATH YOU LEARN, THE MORE MATH YOU SEE...

SO WHAT DO I OWE YOU FOR ALL THIS?

LET'S SEE... THREE HOURS OF MATH TUTORING AT 75¢ PER HOUR...

THAT COMES TO $31.50.

I THINK YOU MEAN $2.25.

BRA-VO! YOU PASSED YOUR FINAL TEST! WELL DONE, PAIGE!

RATS.

PETER FOX TAKES THE HANDOFF AND STREAKS DOWNFIELD!

WITH UNHEARD-OF SPEED, HE PUTS THE DEFENSE TO SHAME! REGGIE WHITE BOUNCES OFF! CHARLES HALEY BOUNCES OFF! DERRICK THOMAS BOUNCES OFF!

AMEND

THE KID IS AMAZING! NO ONE CAN STOP HIM!

HOMEWORK. NOW.

NO ONE **EXCEPT**...

MOM, CAN I HAVE SOME MONEY TO GO TO THE MOVIES?

WHAT HAPPENED TO YOUR ALLOWANCE?

I SPENT IT ALL. PLEEEASE?

PETER, THIS IS WHY PEOPLE MAKE BUDGETS. YOU HAVE TO PRIORITIZE AND LIMIT YOUR SPENDING. IF YOU REALLY WANTED TO SEE A MOVIE, YOU SHOULD HAVE SET ASIDE SOME MONEY FOR IT. I'M SORRY, BUT NO.

BUT **MOM**...

NO. I WANT YOU TO **LEARN** SOMETHING FROM THIS.

...THAT FROM NOW ON, I ASK DAD.

IS $10 ENOUGH?

QUINCY, FETCH!

QUINCY, **DON'T** FETCH!

AMEND

ATTA BOY!

UNREAL...

18

FoxTrot
BILL AMEND

SLURRP...

PAIGE MADE THE COFFEE, I TAKE IT.

HOW'D YOU GUESS?

TRY TO IDENTIFY THE SECRET INGREDIENT.

LET'S SEE... WHAT DO I WANT TO DO TODAY?...

I COULD PLAY COMPUTER GAMES...

I COULD SORT MY "STAR TREK" TRADING CARDS...

WAS THIS COMIC BOOK YOURS?

I COULD PLAN THE PERFECT MURDER...

AT LEAST I DIDN'T SPILL **CHOCOLATE** MILK...

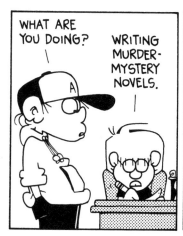

WHAT ARE YOU DOING?

WRITING MURDER-MYSTERY NOVELS.

UM, IS THERE A PARTICULAR REASON **WHY**?

IT'S GREAT! I CAN DREAM UP ALL SORTS OF SINISTER CRIMES, I'LL NEVER GET IN TROUBLE, AND WITH LUCK I'LL MAKE LOTS OF MONEY.

CHECK OUT MY LIST OF POSSIBLE TITLES.

DON'T BE SO SURE ABOUT THAT "NEVER GET IN TROUBLE" PART.

I ESPECIALLY LOOK FORWARD TO WRITING "PAIGE'S MURDER ON THE ORIENT EXPRESS" AND "PAIGE'S DEATH ON THE NILE."

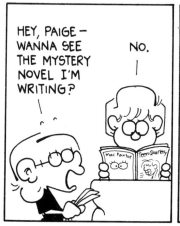

HEY, PAIGE — WANNA SEE THE MYSTERY NOVEL I'M WRITING?

NO.

C'MON, DON'T YOU WANT TO SEE EVEN A **LITTLE** OF IT?

NO!

PLEEEASE? ARE YOU **SURE** YOU DON'T WANT TO SEE IT?

OK, OK! I'LL LOOK AT IT!

TOUGH. IT'S TOP SECRET. BA HA HA HA HA!

SPEAKING OF MYSTERIES...

20

"Press 'M' for Murder"
by Jason Fox

Paige Fox enters her bedroom as she does every day after school. Suddenly, a 16-ton weight falls from the ceiling and squishes her dead!!!

The End

HMM. SOMETHING'S MISSING...

... a 16-ton weight with razor-sharp spikes...

I HEAR YOU'RE WRITING MURDER MYSTERIES.

YUP. I'M WORKING ON MY SEVENTH ONE NOW.

GOSH, A REGULAR J.B. FLETCHER!

WHO'S THAT?

JESSICA FLETCHER. ANGELA LANSBURY'S CHARACTER ON "MURDER, SHE WROTE."

I MEAN, IN TERMS OF PROLIFICACY.

It was then that the killer spotted his <u>next</u> victim...

PETER SAYS THAT IN ALL YOUR LITTLE MYSTERY STORIES, **I'M** THE ONE WHO GETS MURDERED!

NOT TRUE!

WHILE I ADMIT I KILL YOU OFF IN "PAIGE FALLS DOWN THE 39 STEPS," "PAIGE'S MURDER IN THE RUE MORGUE" AND "PAIGE'S BODY IN THE LIBRARY," IN THIS NEW ONE I'VE ACTUALLY MADE YOU THE **KILLER.**

"PAIGE OF THE BASKERVILLES."

THERE'S JUST NO PLEASING SOME PEOPLE.

FoxTrot
BILL AMEND

FoxTrot
BILL AMEND

WELL, DENISE, FOR ONCE I'M TOTALLY ON TOP OF THINGS.

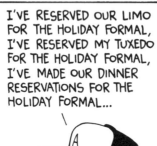

I'VE RESERVED OUR LIMO FOR THE HOLIDAY FORMAL, I'VE RESERVED MY TUXEDO FOR THE HOLIDAY FORMAL, I'VE MADE OUR DINNER RESERVATIONS FOR THE HOLIDAY FORMAL...

THERE WAS SOMETHING I STILL NEEDED TO DO... WHAT WAS IT?

ASK ME TO **GO** WITH YOU, MAYBE?

OH, YEAH—WHAT KIND OF CORSAGE DO YOU WANT?

PETER, I CAN'T BELIEVE YOU'VE MADE ALL THESE PLANS FOR THE HOLIDAY FORMAL!

WHY?

YOU HAVEN'T EVEN ASKED ME TO **GO** WITH YOU!

OH.

I MEAN, JUST BECAUSE I'M YOUR GIRLFRIEND DOESN'T MEAN YOU CAN TAKE ME FOR GRANTED! TALK ABOUT **INSULTING**! I'M NOT **ALWAYS** A SURE THING, YOU KNOW!

OK, OK, I'M SORRY. DENISE, WILL YOU GO TO THE DANCE WITH ME?

YES. BUT UNDER PROTEST.

NOW, THEN, OUR DINNER RESERVATIONS ARE FOR 7:30...

HI, PETER? IT'S ME, DENISE.

YO. WHAT'S UP?

I JUST FOUND OUT THAT MY PARENTS ARE TAKING ME UP TO VISIT MY GRANDMOTHER THE SAME WEEKEND AS THE HOLIDAY FORMAL.

CAN'T YOU GET OUT OF IT?

WELL, SHE'S KINDA GETTING UP THERE IN YEARS. I THINK IT'S PROBABLY JUST A LITTLE MORE IMPORTANT FOR ME TO SPEND TIME WITH HER THAN TO GO TO A DANCE.

OH.

EVEN A DANCE WITH **ME**?

AS HARD AS THE CONCEPT MIGHT BE FOR YOU TO GRASP...

Panel 1: AAAA! WHY DOES THIS SORT OF THING ALWAYS HAPPEN TO ME?!

WHAT?

Panel 2: DENISE BAGGED ON THE HOLIDAY FORMAL! MY OWN GIRLFRIEND! I'M DATELESS!

SO?

Panel 3: SO?! I'VE GOT A LIMO LINED UP... DINNER LINED UP... A TUXEDO LINED UP... A CORSAGE LINED UP... ALL OF IT **WASTED**! IT'S NOT LIKE I CAN JUST TAKE SOMEBODY ELSE!

Panel 4: MONOGAMY STINKS.

SPEAKING AS A **NO**GAMIST...

Panel 5: I HEAR DENISE CAN'T GO TO THE BIG DANCE WITH YOU.

THANK YOU, BLABBERMOUTH PAIGE!

Panel 6: IT'S NOT THE END OF THE WORLD, PETER. THERE'LL BE OTHER DANCES.

I KNOW, BUT I HAD THIS ONE ALL PLANNED! NOW I HAVE TO CANCEL THE LIMO, CANCEL THE FLORIST, CANCEL THE TUXEDO... IT'S A TOTAL PAIN IN THE REAR!

Panel 7: MAYBE YOU COULD TAKE SOMEONE ELSE?

ARE YOU KIDDING? I'D **DIE**!

Panel 8: YOUR FEELINGS FOR DENISE ARE THAT STRONG?

HER TANTRUMS ARE.

Panel 9: PETER, I HAVE TO GO VISIT MY GRANDMOTHER. I'M SORRY.

SO I'M SUPPOSED TO GO TO THIS DANCE BY **MYSELF**?!

BE STILL MY HEART.

MINDY, DON'T EVEN **THINK** IT.

FoxTrot
BILL AMEND

Dear, Dear, Dear,

Dear, Dear, Dear,
Dear, Dear, Dear, Dear,
Dear, Dear, Dear,

Dear Santa,

For Christmas this year,
I'd like the following:

A tarantula,

A boa constrictor,

And a large,
gray rat.

I hope you'll come
through for me. I'd be
the happiest kid alive.

Sincerely,
Paige Fox

SMEAR SOME CLEARASIL ON IT FOR ADDED REALISM.

WHAT ARE YOU SMURFS UP TO?

MINDY, YOU'LL GET OVER ME SOMEDAY, I'M SURE OF IT.

YOU MAY NOT THINK SO NOW, YOU MAY NOT THINK SO TOMORROW, BUT EVENTUALLY YOU'LL FORGET ALL ABOUT STUPID PETER FOX AND HOW MUCH HE HURT YOU.

YOU JUST GOTTA HANG IN THERE, KIDDO. BROKEN HEARTS DO HEAL.

ARE YOU LISTENING TO ME?

...SO THEN AFTER THE DANCE, I THOUGHT MAYBE WE COULD GO OUT FOR ICE CREAM...

I KNOW JUST THE PLACE...

UNBELIEVABLE. IT'S UNNNN-BELIEVABLE.

WHAT IS?

YOU KNOW HOW I'VE BEEN GOING NUTS ALL WEEK TRYING TO FIGURE OUT WHAT TO DO ABOUT THIS GIRL WHO ASKED ME TO THE FORMAL?

YEAH, SO?

WELL, ALONG COMES MY FRIEND STEVE, I INTRODUCE THEM, AND KAPOW, THEY'RE IN LOVE. I MEAN GA-GA CITY. NOW **HE'S** GOING TO THE DANCE WITH HER. IT'S SIMPLY UNBELIEVABLE!

THAT YOUR IMPOSSIBLE SITUATION ACTUALLY WORKED OUT?

THAT HER CRUSH ON ME COULD BE SO FLEETING.

STILL, YOUR EGO SEEMS UNSCATHED.

PETER, I'M SORRY I WAS SUCH A CRY-BABY ABOUT ALL THIS.

DENISE, DON'T WORRY ABOUT IT.

IT'S JUST THAT THE THOUGHT OF YOU POSSIBLY GOING TO THE HOLIDAY FORMAL WITH ANOTHER GIRL, WELL, IT KINDA RIPPED ME UP INSIDE.

I KNOW. I'M SORRY. I PROBABLY SHOULD'VE BEEN MORE MINDFUL OF YOUR FEELINGS.

AT LEAST THINGS WORKED OUT FOR EVERYBODY.

STEVE'S TAKING MINDY TO THE DANCE AND PAYING ME FOR THE LIMO DEPOSIT, YOU GET TO VISIT YOUR GRANDMOTHER WITHOUT HAVING TO WORRY ABOUT ME, AND I GET TO SPEND SATURDAY NIGHT HERE AT HOME.

OK... FOR **ALMOST** EVERYBODY.

JASON, I SAID **LATER**.

"SUPER MARIO UNIVERSE 2" AWAITS...

33

FoxTrot
BILL AMEND

MOM, CAN YOU KEEP AN EYE ON QUINCY FOR A WHILE?

WHAT FOR?

I'M WRAPPING CHRISTMAS PRESENTS IN MY ROOM AND I DON'T WANT HIM TO SEE WHAT I GOT HIM.

OF ALL THE TIMES TO BE LEFT SPEECHLESS.

YOU CAN FEED HIM SOME CRICKETS IF HE BEHAVES HIMSELF.

WOW! I CAN'T BELIEVE DAD GOT ME A BEAVIS STOCKING!

I CAN'T BELIEVE DAD GOT ME A BUTT-HEAD ONE!

HUH-HUH HUH-HUH M HUH HNNGH M HNNGH HUH M HUH-HUH-HUH M HUH-HUH HUH-HUH M HUH HNNGH HUH HUH-HUH HUH HUH M HUH HNNGH HUH M HUH-HUH

THEY CAN'T BELIEVE IT?!?

THE WOMAN AT THE STORE SAID THEY WERE QUITE THE RAGE.

LET ME SHOW YOU RAGE.

DID YOU SEE THE MISTLETOE I PUT UP?

WHAT'S WITH ALL THESE MAGAZINES?

I TELL YOU, THERE'S NOTHING WORSE THAN GOING SHOPPING TWO DAYS BEFORE CHRISTMAS...

...AT THE LARGEST MALL IN TOWN...

...WITH PAIGE.

EXCEPT MAYBE GOING ONE DAY BEFORE CHRISTMAS.

GOD FORBID.

HEY, PETER—WHAT ARE YOU DOING TOMORROW?

DAD, WE NEED A FAX MACHINE.

WHY'S THAT?

WELL, I'VE GOT THIS LAST-MINUTE ADDENDUM TO MY CHRISTMAS LIST AND IT'S TOO LATE TO GET IT TO SANTA ANY OTHER WAY. IF WE HAD A FAX, I'D BE ALL SET.

ALSO, IF WE HAD ONE, I COULD SEND NEAT-O CARTOONS AND MESSAGES TO YOU AT WORK EVERY DAY.

I'D LIKE TO RETURN THIS, IF POSSIBLE.

I THOUGHT YOUR WIFE REALLY WANTED ONE.

FAXMASTER 550

TO A MERRY CHRISTMAS, EVERYONE!

EEW! WHAT'S IN THIS EGGNOG?!

WHOOPS. THAT WAS MEANT FOR PAIGE.

LET'S SEE... SALAD FORK OR DINNER FORK?

...AND A MORE PEACEFUL NEW YEAR.

36

FoxTrot
BILL AMEND

HEY, PETER— WANNA DRIVE ME TO THE MALL?

WHAT FOR?

I WANT TO BUY A VIDEO GAME CARTRIDGE WITH MY CHRISTMAS MONEY.

WHICH GAME?

I'D RATHER NOT SAY. I'D HATE FOR YOU TO GET IN TROUBLE WITH MOM AND DAD FOR BEING A KNOWING ACCESSORY TO THIS PURCHASE.

AMEND

OF COURSE, THAT ALONE TELLS ME TOO MUCH.

LET'S JUST SAY V-GAMER DIGEST GAVE IT FOUR SEVERED THUMBS UP.

SALE!!! ALL SEGA & NINTENDO CARTRIDGES 0.5% OFF!

I CAN'T BELIEVE I'M ACTUALLY THE PROUD OWNER OF "MORTAL KARNAGE II."

THIS IS THE VIDEO GAME THAT WOWED 'EM SPEECHLESS AT THIS YEAR'S VIDGAMCON EXPO. IT'S GOT 17 LEVELS OF ESCALATING BLOODLETTING, DIGITALLY SAMPLED SCREAMS AND SPLATTERS AND, OF COURSE, THE NEW AND IMPROVED DECAPITATION ROUND.

VIOLENCE UNMATCHED ANYWHERE.

ARE YOU TALKING ABOUT THE GAME OR MOM'S LIKELY REACTION?

HEY, IF THIS WERE SO BAD FOR KIDS, THEY WOULDN'T SELL IT TO KIDS, RIGHT?

AMEND

C'MON, POP IT IN.

PETER, YOU CAN'T PLAY A GAME OF "MORTAL KARNAGE II'S" COMPLEXITY WITHOUT FIRST READING THE INSTRUCTION MANUAL.

LET'S SEE... TO THROW A BASIC PUNCH, HOLD DOWN THE "B," "C" AND "X" BUTTONS, TAP THE "START" BUTTON, USE THE ARROW PAD TO INDICATE DIRECTION AND RELEASE THE "C" BUTTON WHEN THE FORCE BAR TOPS 80 PERCENT.

AMEND

THAT'S A **BASIC** PUNCH?!

WHOOPS. THAT WAS AN UPPER-CUT. THE BASIC PUNCH DOESN'T USE THE "X" BUTTON.

ALREADY THIS GAME IS MAKING REAL-LIFE FIGHTING SEEM ATTRACTIVE.

HERE'S A FOLD-OUT CHART SHOWING HOW TO KICK...

OK, I'M ENTERING THE TEMPLE OF THE DRAGON LORD...

NOW, IF A NINJA SHOWS UP, I HAVE TO RIGHT AWAY DOUBLE-CLICK ON THE "A" BUTTON TO RIP HIS THROAT OUT...

IF A HIGH PRIEST SHOWS UP, I DO A BACK FLIP AND KICK HIS HEAD OFF... AND IF A NECRO-SAMURAI SHOWS UP, I USE MY NEUTRO-BLAST TO BREAK ALL HIS BONES.

WHAT IF MOM SHOWS UP?

HIDE THE CARTRIDGE AND LIE LIKE A RUG. WHY?

JASON, WHAT'S THIS?

MOM, WHAT ARE YOU DOING?!

TAKING AWAY THIS VIDEO GAME CARTRIDGE, FOR STARTERS.

BUT YOU CAN'T! I BOUGHT IT WITH MY CHRISTMAS MONEY! IT'S MINE!

JASON, I TOLD YOU TWO WEEKS AGO THAT I DIDN'T WANT "MORTAL KARNAGE II" COMING INTO THIS HOUSE. YOU HAVE NO ONE TO BLAME BUT YOURSELF.

BUT... BUT...

YOU'RE TOO YOUNG FOR THIS SORT OF THING. I MEAN, LOOK AT WHAT IT TEACHES: THAT HUMAN DISEMBOWELMENT IS ENTERTAINMENT... THAT "WINNERS" DECAPITATE THEIR ENEMIES... THAT CARNAGE IS SPELLED WITH A "K"...

I KNOW CARNAGE ISN'T SPELLED WITH A "K."

THE SAD PART IS, THAT'S THE LEAST OF MY CONCERNS.

MOM, I'VE GIVEN IT SOME THOUGHT, AND YOU'RE RIGHT— I'M TOO YOUNG FOR A VIDEO GAME LIKE "MORTAL KARNAGE II."

I GET FAR TOO MUCH VIOLENCE IN MY DAILY MEDIA DIET AS IT IS. I DON'T NEED TO REVEL IN SOME ELECTRONIC BLOODSPORT FOR FUN. CHILDHOOD IS FLEETING ENOUGH WITHOUT ME WASTING MY DAYS GLUED TO A TV SCREEN.

JASON, THOSE ARE VERY MATURE OBSERVATIONS. I'M IMPRESSED.

MATURE ENOUGH TO GET ME BACK MY "MORTAL KARNAGE II" CARTRIDGE?

CAN'T BLAME ME FOR TRYING.

OH, YES I CAN.

FoxTrot
BILL AMEND

PAIGE MUST BE COOKING DINNER.

I'LL GO OPEN A WINDOW.

DINER EST SERVI!

WE'RE JUST GONNA EAT CEREAL.

NO WAY, BUCKOS. JUST BECAUSE MOM AND DAD ARE GONE DOESN'T MEAN YOU CAN EAT FROOT LOOPS FOR DINNER!

I SLAVED ALL AFTERNOON MAKING THIS MEAL AND YOU'RE GOING TO EAT IT!

NOW, THEN, DO YOU WANT A LOT OF SPAGHETTI OR A LITTLE SPAGHETTI?

CHUNK! CHUNK! CHUNK!

THAT'S SPAGHETTI?!?

OH, WAIT—THIS IS THE PEACH COBBLER.

I THINK WE HAVE HERE THE MAKINGS OF A KILLER WEIGHT-LOSS PROGRAM.

EMPHASIS ON "KILLER."

TWEEE!

RELAX—IT'S JUST THE SMOKE ALARM.

AMEND

FoxTrot
BILL AMEND

MOM, I HAVE TO WRITE AN ESSAY ON "MACBETH" AND I THOUGHT MAYBE YOU COULD HELP ME WITH IT.

"MACBETH"? YOU'RE STUDYING "MACBETH"?

"IS THIS A DAGGER WHICH I SEE BEFORE ME, THE HANDLE TOWARD MY HAND?... I GO, AND IT IS DONE; THE BELL INVITES ME. HEAR IT NOT, DUNCAN; FOR IT IS A KNELL THAT SUMMONS THEE TO HEAVEN OR TO HELL!"

THAT "MACBETH"?

I KEEP FORGETTING YOU WERE AN ENGLISH MAJOR.

ACT I. SCENE I.- AN OPEN PLACE. THUNDER AND LIGHTNING. ENTER THREE WITCHES...

MOM, LOOK, "MACBETH" MAY GET YOU ALL EXCITED, BUT TO ME IT'S JUST A PLAY.

JUST A PLAY?!

JUST A PLAY?!

ONE OF SHAKESPEARE'S GREATEST AND DARKEST AND RELEVANT TRAGEDIES AND YOU CONSIDER IT JUST A **PLAY**?!

OK, A PLAY AND A SPIT SHIELD.

DID YOU BREAK THAT BINDING?

ANYWAY, I KINDA HOPED YOU COULD HELP ME WITH THIS "MACBETH" ESSAY I HAVE TO WRITE.

HAVING TROUBLE COMING UP WITH A GOOD THESIS?

HAVING TROUBLE COMING UP WITH KEY EXAMPLES SUPPORTING YOUR THESIS?

HAVING TROUBLE WRAPPING IT ALL UP WITH A STRONG AND CLEAR CONCLUSION?

UM, WHAT'S "MACBETH" ABOUT?

IT'S ABOUT 100 PAGES. NOW GET GOING.

WELL, IT'S TAKEN TWO DAYS...

THREE HOURS AND 28 MINUTES...

BUT I'VE FINALLY FINISHED...

...READING PAGE ONE.

YOU KNOW, THEY CAN **PERFORM** THESE PLAYS IN TWO HOURS...

I FINISHED READING "MACBETH"... I FINISHED READING "MACBETH"...

NOW I CAN START WRITING MY ESSAY...

TALK ABOUT MOOD SWINGS.

AND IT'S DUE IN 14 HOURS.

MOM, CAN YOU HELP ME WITH MY "MACBETH" ESSAY?

PAIGE, WE'VE BEEN THROUGH THIS ALL WEEK!

I'M NOT GOING TO TELL YOU WHAT THE PLAY IS ABOUT! I'M NOT GOING TO BUY YOU THE CLIFFS NOTES! I'M NOT GOING TO TELL YOU WHAT TOPIC TO CHOOSE AND I'M NOT GOING TO WRITE HALF YOUR SENTENCES FOR YOU! I'M SORRY! THE POINT OF THIS ASSIGNMENT IS FOR **YOU** TO DO THE WORK!

JUST DOUBLE-CHECK MY SPELLING.

WHY DIDN'T YOU JUST **SAY** SO?

I LIKE TO WATCH YOUR CHEW-OUTS FALL FLAT.

PAIGE, HOW DO YOU SPELL "MACBETH"?

44

FoxTrot
BILL AMEND

HEY, PETER — TRIVIA TIME. WHAT'S THE CAPITAL OF BELGIUM?

UM, BRUSSELS.

NORWAY? OSLO.
ITALY? ROME.
SWITZERLAND? BERN.
THE CZECH REPUBLIC? PRAGUE.

ARE YOU SURE??

DEFINITELY.

HOMEWORK'S DONE.

WHAT'S "PROG"?

AMEND

♪ MIGHTY MORPHIN POWER RANGERS...

♪ MIGHTY MORPHIN POWER RANGERS...

♪ MIGHTY MORPHIN POW—...

YOU GUYS CALL THAT "MIGHTY"?!

THEY CERTAINLY "MORPHED"..

AMEND

PAIGE, YOU HAVE A CALL FROM SOMEONE NAMED STACY.

ICK! IT'S THAT CREEPY STACY ROGERS!

TELL HER I'M BUSY! TELL HER I'M NOT HOME! TELL HER I HAVE LARYNGITIS! TELL HER ANYTHING!

AMEND

I'D SAY YOU'VE TOLD HER PLENTY ALREADY.

Ahem.

I JUST LOVE CORDLESS PHONES.

HEH HEH, **STACY**!... WHAT A PLEASANT SURPRISE!..

47

FoxTrot
BILL AMEND

MOM, CAN YOU HELP US SETTLE AN ARGUMENT? WHO'S THE COOLEST OF THE X-MEN — CYCLOPS OR WOLVERINE?

WOLVERINE. DEFINITELY.

HA! SEE?!

NOW LET ME WORK.

YOUR MOM'S PRETTY COOL.

FOR A MOM.

ROGER, OUT OF CURIOSITY, WHO THE **HECK** ARE THE X-MEN?

HMM?

MMM — HONEY, THIS IS DELICIOUS!

I MEAN, THE SAUCE IS OUT OF THIS WORLD!

BOY, IS THIS A FAR CRY FROM THE LASAGNA YOU **USED** TO MAKE!

DAD, THIS IS TAKEOUT.

I MEAN, UM, "A FAR CRY" IN THE DIFFERENT-BUT-EQUALLY-YUMMY SENSE...

THE REAL QUESTION IS HOW DOES YOUR **FOOT** TASTE?

HEY, PAIGE, HAPPY GROUNDHOG DAY.

AAAA!

SORRY. I DIDN'T HAVE A GROUNDHOG.

SUDDENLY, I WISH IT WERE ARMISTICE DAY...

THAT'S NOT TILL NOVEMBER, PAL.

PETER, I WAS MAKING YOUR BED TODAY AND GUESS WHAT I FOUND UNDER YOUR MATTRESS?...

MOM, I CAN EXPLAIN!

I JUST HAVE THOSE MAGAZINES FOR THE ARTICLES! I **SWEAR!**

I WAS TALKING ABOUT YOUR NEW BASEBALL MITT.

OH. UM, THAT'S HOW YOU BREAK IT IN.

NOW, WHAT'S THIS ABOUT MAGAZINES?

YOU MEAN MY SCIENTIFIC AMERICAN COLLECTION?...

ICK. HOW CAN YOU EAT THAT STUFF?

SUGAR-FROSTED HONEY FLAKES?

THEY'RE NOTHING BUT SUGAR AND ARTIFICIAL CHEMICALS! I MEAN, LOOK AT YOUR MILK-IT'S TURNED INTO SOME PURPLISH OOZE!

IT IS PRETTY DISGUSTING.

SO THEN WHY DO YOU EAT SIX BOWLS OF IT EVERY MORNING?!

FOR THE GLOW-IN-THE-DARK DINOSAUR STICKERS.

ACTUALLY, I'M A LITTLE SURPRISED THAT **YOU** DON'T GLOW IN THE DARK BY NOW.

IN ANOTHER MONTH, I'LL HAVE WALLPAPERED MY ROOM.

LET'S GO, GUYS. IT'S PAST YOUR BEDTIME.

BUT... BUT...

NO "BUTS." LET'S GO. UPSTAIRS.

BUT "BLOOD ZOMBIES FROM PLANET X" JUST **STARTED!** WE CAN'T TURN IT OFF **NOW!**

OH, YES YOU CAN.

BUT WE JUST DRANK A SIX-PACK OF COLA. EACH.

WELCOME TO THE **REAL** LATE-NIGHT TELEVISION WAR.

PLEASE? PLEASE? PLEASE? PLEASE? PLEASE? PLEASE? PLEEEEEEEEASE?

A THREE POINTER AT THE BUZZER...

IT'S GOOD! HOLY COW! THEY WIN!

YES! YES! YES! YES! YES! YES! YES! YES! YES! YES!

HOO BOY, AM I WINDED.

YOU KNOW, WHEN YOU'RE NOT EVEN IN GOOD ENOUGH SHAPE TO **WATCH** BASKETBALL...

AEROBICS?! ME?! ARE YOU CRAZY?!

IT'LL BE GOOD FOR YOU.

AEROBICS?! ME?! ARE YOU CRAZY?!

ROGER, YOU'RE TOTALLY OUT OF SHAPE. FACE IT.

AEROBICS?! ME?! ARE YOU CRAZY?!

WE'LL GO TOGETHER. IT'LL BE FUN.

HELLOOOO, SPANDEX...

I **MUST** BE CRAZY.

HI, YOU MUST BE NEW. I'M TINA, YOUR AEROBICS INSTRUCTOR.

HI... I'M... ROGER...

HEE HEE... FORGIVE ME IF... I'M A LITTLE OUT OF BREATH... IT'S BEEN A... WHILE SINCE I'VE DONE ANY REAL... EXERCISE...

I GUESS YOU COULD SAY... I'M A TAD OUT OF... SHAPE...

CERTAINLY CONSIDERING THAT WE HAVEN'T EVEN **STARTED**.

I KINDA JOGGED UP THE FRONT STAIRS.

HERE'S SOME MORE WATER.

I SWEAR, IF JASON DOESN'T START CLEANING UP HIS ROOM...

WHAT'S THIS?

Dear Gretchen,
I think you're the prettiest girl in the school. Please be my valentine.
Love,
Jason

DID ANYONE ELSE JUST HEAR A LOUD "THUD"?

AMEND

JASON WROTE A **LOVE** LETTER?! I SAW IT ON HIS DESK! IT WAS ADDRESSED TO SOMEONE NAMED GRETCHEN!

IT SAID HE THOUGHT SHE WAS THE PRETTIEST GIRL IN THE SCHOOL AND HE ENDED IT "LOVE, JASON." NOW, WHAT DO **YOU** CALL THAT?!

THE END OF AN ERA... OUR BABY'S GROWING UP...

IT SEEMS LIKE JUST YESTERDAY HE WAS CALLING GIRLS "REPUL-SOIDS" AND "BOOG-O-TRONS." ACTUALLY, IT WAS THIS MORNING.

AMEND

WELL, I'VE GONE THROUGH JASON'S YEARBOOK FROM LAST YEAR AND I CAN'T FIND A SINGLE GIRL NAMED GRETCHEN.

OF COURSE, THAT DOESN'T MEAN SHE COULDN'T BE NEW THIS YEAR, OR MAYBE GRETCHEN IS A MIDDLE NAME OR SOMETHING.

I SUPPOSE I COULD CALL THE SCHOOL AND HAVE THEM CHECK THEIR RECORDS. WHAT DO YOU THINK?

WHY DON'T YOU JUST ASK **JASON** WHO SHE IS? AND HAVE HIM THINK I'M **NOSEY**?!

AMEND

MOM, WHAT'S WRONG?

OH, I'M JUST FLOUNDERING IN ONE OF MY USUAL PARENTAL DILEMMAS.

A FEW DAYS AGO, I STUMBLED ACROSS A VALENTINE'S DAY CARD THAT JASON HAD WRITTEN TO SOME GIRL AT HIS SCHOOL NAMED GRETCHEN. IT WAS, SHALL WE SAY, OF A ROMANTIC NATURE.

JASON?! THIS IS JASON?!

ANYWAY, I'M DYING TO FIND OUT MORE ABOUT THIS GIRL, BUT I DON'T DARE TELL HIM THAT I—...

JASON AND GRETCHEN, SITTIN' IN A TREE...

...KNOW.

WHO TOLD YOU ABOUT GRETCHEN?

JASON, SWEETIE, I SAW THE VALENTINE'S DAY CARD YOU MADE FOR HER.

IT'S PRETTY OBVIOUS THAT YOU LIKE HER A LOT, AND I JUST WANT YOU TO KNOW THAT IT'S OK. NO ONE IS GOING TO MAKE FUN OF YOU.

I JUST WISH YOU'D **TELL** US ABOUT HER.

WELL, SHE HAS THIS GREAT WAY OF EATING MICE...

DID YOU SAY MICE?

ARE WE ALLOWED TO MAKE FUN OF GRETCHEN?

GRETCHEN'S A **SNAKE**?!

SHE'S MISS O'MALLEY'S BOA CONSTRICTOR.

YOU MADE THAT VALENTINE'S DAY CARD FOR A **SNAKE**?!

WHO'D YOU THINK IT WAS FOR?

WELL, FOR STARTERS, A **GIRL**.

EEW! GROSS! ICK! WHAT KIND OF A WEIRDO DO YOU THINK I AM?!

DON'T ASK.

WOULD IT BE OK IF MARCUS AND I BUILT AN ANDROID THIS WEEKEND?

FoxTrot
BILL AMEND

DG JQZLF RGLP HQIR?

PETER, WHAT ARE YOU DOING?

GQLMN BDOG SNGM.

WHAT?!

KRMLVR BLMQ ZMSOLN.

WHAT?!

GETTING IN SHAPE FOR BASEBALL SEASON.

AS THRILLED AS I AM THAT YOU'RE ONLY CHEWING GUM...

JASON, MOVE IT. I HAVE TO WRITE A PAPER.

TOUGH. I'M PLAYING "IRON MYSTICUS."

WHAT'S THAT?

IT'S THIS COOL NEW CD-ROM COMPUTER GAME. YOU ROAM AROUND AN ALIEN WORLD FINDING CLUES AND SOLVING PUZZLES WHILE BEING STALKED BY A KILLER ROBOT.

WHEN WILL YOU BE DONE?

HARD TO SAY. A GAME LIKE THIS MIGHT GO ON FOREVER.

GUESS NOT.

HEY! WHAT HAPPENED TO MY "PAIGE'S HOMEWORK" FOLDER?!

SIGH.

SHE'S LOOKING AT ME!

SHE'S LOOKING AT ME!

SHE'S LOOKING AT ME!

SHE'S LOOKING AT ME!

BURP.

AAAA! WHO TAPED OVER "MELROSE PLACE"?!

HEY, DON'T BLAME ME.

YOU LEFT THE TAPE IN THE MACHINE, DUMMY. WHEN YOU RECORD SOMETHING, YOU SHOULD EITHER WATCH IT RIGHT AWAY OR TAKE OUT THE CASSETTE. HOW AM I SUPPOSED TO KNOW WHAT YOU'VE SEEN AND WHAT YOU HAVEN'T?!

YOU RECORDED A BASKETBALL GAME?

AAAA! WHO TAPED OVER "BABYLON 5"?!

HEY, DON'T BLAME ME.

I SHOOT AN ARROW INTO THE AIR...

...IT FALLS TO EARTH, AND I KNOW WHERE.

POETRY FOR PHYSICISTS.

USA! USA! USA! USA! USA! USA! USA! USA! USA! USA!

I HAVE A SINKING FEELING WE MAY BE PRE-EMPTED TONIGHT.

WEIRDOS.

FoxTrot
BILL AMEND

JASON FOX IS OUR NEXT $10 MILLION WINNER!!!

I WON $10 MILLION! I WON $10 MILLION! I'M RICH! I'M RICH! I WON $10 MILLION!

ODD THAT THEY WOULD SEND SUCH IMPORTANT NEWS VIA BULK RATE MAIL.

LOOK, QUINCY— "JASON FOX IS OUR NEXT $10 MILLION WINNER"!

I'M RICH! I'M RICH! I'M FILTHY, STINKING RICH!

I CAN'T BELIEVE I WON THE SWEEPSTAKES! I CAN'T BELIEVE THEY REALLY PICKED ME!

ESPECIALLY SINCE I CAN'T RECALL EVER SENDING IN AN ENTRY.

MOM! LOOK! I WON $10 MILLION!

SEE?! IT SAYS SO ON THE ENVELOPE: "JASON FOX IS OUR NEXT $10 MILLION WINNER"!

JASON FOX IS OUR NEXT $10 MILLION WINNER!!!

IMAGINE ALL THE WONDER- FUL THINGS THIS MONEY WILL LET ME DO!

I THINK I'LL GO LAUGH IN MY UGLY SISTER'S FACE.

I'VE GOT TO GET AN OFFICE OUTSIDE OF THIS HOUSE.

I CAN'T BELIEVE I ACTUALLY WON $10 MILLION!

I SUPPOSE AT THIS POINT I SHOULD FIND MYSELF A GOOD FINANCIAL ADVISER.

SOMEONE WITH EXPERIENCE HANDLING LARGE BLOCKS OF MONEY...

GLAD YOU COULD COME OVER, MR. $5-A-WEEK ALLOWANCE.

WHAT'S THE EMERGENCY?

YOU KNOW, I'LL BET I'M THE FIRST KID FROM OUR SCHOOL TO WIN A $10 MILLION DRAWING.

HEY—YOU NEVER OPENED THE ENVELOPE.

I WAS TOO EXCITED. IT'S PROBABLY JUST FULL OF LEGAL FORMS AND INSTRUCTIONS ON HOW TO PICK UP MY MONEY. LET'S TAKE A LOOK...

RIP RIP RIP

JASON FOX IS OUR NEXT $10 MILLION WINNER!!!

...IF ENTRY NUMBER X10J7680T3 IS SELECTED IN OUR SWEEP-STAKES DRAWING.

MAYBE I SHOULD TELL IBM TO PUT A HOLD ON THAT ORDER...

YOU MIGHT ALSO WANT TO CALL BACK THAT REALTOR LADY...

MOM, I JUST FOUND OUT I DIDN'T WIN $10 MILLION AFTER ALL.

I KNOW, SWEETIE. I'M SORRY.

I THOUGHT FOR SURE I HAD. I MEAN, THE ENVELOPE SAID, "JASON FOX IS OUR NEXT $10 MILLION WINNER." ISN'T THAT LYING?

THEY CALL IT MARKETING.

IF YOU KNEW I DIDN'T WIN, WHY DIDN'T YOU TELL ME?

YOU WERE SO HAPPY. I FIGURED IT COULDN'T HURT TO LET YOU THINK YOU WERE A MILLIONAIRE FOR A FEW HOURS.

WHAT DO YOU MEAN BY "UM"?

UM...

MOM, THERE'S A HERSHEY TRUCK BACKING INTO OUR DRIVEWAY!

FoxTrot
BILL AMEND

WHO WANTS COFFEE?

ME!

ME!

ME!

THEN I'LL GO MAKE SOME.

NEVER MIND.

NEVER MIND.

NEVER MIND.

MOM, HOW DO YOU USE THE NEW COFFEE MAKER?

WELL, LET'S SEE... FIRST YOU MAKE SURE EVERYTHING'S CLEAN...

THEN YOU PUT A FILTER IN THE BASKET... MEASURE OUT THE GROUND COFFEE INTO THE FILTER...

PUT THE BASKET BACK INTO ITS SLOT, POUR YOUR WATER INTO THE TOP AND HIT THE "ON" SWITCH.

IT'S REALLY PRETTY SIMPLE.

EEW! PAIGE, WHAT IS THIS?!

GO BACK TO THAT PART ABOUT A FILTER...

YOU KNOW, WE DO HAVE "INSTANT"...

AMEND

64

MOM! MOM! I'M GOING TO BE WORKING ON THE SCHOOL NEWSPAPER!

PAIGE, THAT'S GREAT!

I'LL BE DOING A "QUESTION WOMAN" COLUMN WHERE I GO AROUND AND GET STUDENTS' OPINIONS ON VARIOUS TOPICS.

OOO...

NO LONGER WILL I SIMPLY BE "PAIGE FOX, ANONYMOUS FRESHMAN"... FROM NOW ON I'LL BE "PAIGE FOX, ALL-POWERFUL QUESTION WOMAN"! THIS IS SO EXCITING!

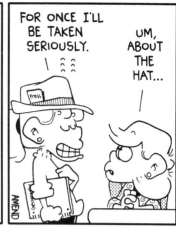

FOR ONCE I'LL BE TAKEN SERIOUSLY.

UM, ABOUT THE HAT...

LET'S SEE... I THINK WE'VE JUST ABOUT COVERED EVERYTHING.

YOU'RE **FOR** U.S. MILITARY INTERVENTION IN BOSNIA, **AGAINST** CONTINUED DEFICIT SPENDING BY CONGRESS AND **AGAINST** USING THE DEATH PENALTY ON MINORS.

CORRECT.

NOW FOR THE TOUGH ONE...

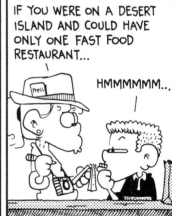

IF YOU WERE ON A DESERT ISLAND AND COULD HAVE ONLY ONE FAST FOOD RESTAURANT...

HMMMMMM...

WOULD YOU MIND IF I POLLED YOU ON A FEW THINGS FOR THE SCHOOL NEWSPAPER?

UM...

UM...

UM...

NEXT!...

COULD YOU REPEAT THE QUESTION?

ONE LAST QUESTION — DO YOU THINK "BEAVIS AND BUTT-HEAD" ARE REALISTIC?

HUH-HUH-HUH...

M HEH-HEH...

HUH-HUH M HUH HUH M HEH-HEH HUH HNNGH M HEH-HEH HUH HUH-HUH-HUH...

HUH-HUH-HUH M HUH-HUH HNNGH HUH M HUH-HUH HEH HUH-HUH-HUH HEH M HUH HNNGH M HUH-HUH HUH-HUH-HUH M HEH-HEH HNNGH M HUH-HUH M HUH HEH-HEH HUH-HUH-HUH...

FORGET I ASKED.

NEVER HEARD OF THEM.

HEH-HEH, SHE SAID "BUTT."

DO YOU MIND IF I ASK YOUR OPINION OF THE PRESIDENT'S HEALTH CARE PLAN?

WELL, LET'S SEE...

I LIKE THE NOTION OF UNIVERSAL COVERAGE AND THE RESULTANT BROADENING OF RISK POOLS.

I HAVE NO PROBLEM WITH EMPLOYER MANDATES, BUT THEN, I'M NOT AN EMPLOYER, SO IT'S EASY FOR ME TO SAY THAT. THE SHORT-TERM COST PROJECTIONS HAVE ME CONCERNED. I WISH I KNEW MORE IN TERMS OF DETAIL AND LESS IN TERMS OF SOUND BITES AND GENERAL-IZATIONS.

SO WOULD THAT BE "THUMBS UP" OR "THUMBS DOWN"?

I'M NOT FINISHED...

MOM, LOOK! MY VERY FIRST COLUMN IN THE SCHOOL PAPER!

OOO— LET ME SEE.

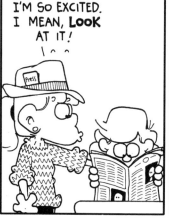

I'M SO EXCITED. I MEAN, **LOOK** AT IT!

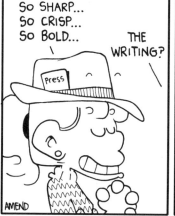

SO SHARP... SO CRISP... SO BOLD...

THE WRITING?

MY **PHOTO!**

IT'S BOLD ALL RIGHT.

FoxTrot
BILL AMEND

I GOT IT! I GOT IT!

THUNK!

I CAUGHT THE BALL! I CAUGHT THE BALL! PETER, DID YOU SEE ME?! I CAUGHT THE BALL!

THEN AGAIN, I THREW THE BALL. JASON, PITCHES ARE SUPPOSED TO TRAVEL TOWARD HOME PLATE.

PETER, THE PITCHER'S MOUND IS TOO FAR AWAY! THEN MOVE IN CLOSER.

HOW CLOSE? I DUNNO. HOW FAR CAN YOU THROW?

I'VE GOT A BAD FEELING ABOUT THIS. JUST BE SURE TO DUCK REALLY FAST.

PTOOIE PTOOIE

SNORT SNORT

PTOOIE PTOOIE

I KNEW THERE HAD TO BE SOME ASPECT OF BASEBALL I LIKED. NOW, IF MOM ASKS, YOU LEARNED THIS FROM TV.

FoxTrot
BILL AMEND

WHY, LOOK! THERE'S A CRIME IN PROGRESS DOWN THERE!

I SAID, DOWN **THERE**!

NO, OVER **THERE**!

OW! OW! OW! WHAT ARE YOU DOING?!

HEY, DON'T BLAME ME — **YOU** RIGGED THE PULLEYS.

WHY COULDN'T WE JUST MAKE A WESTERN?

WHAT ARE YOU PLAYING?

THIS NEW COMPUTER GAME, "PRINCE OF ASSYRIA."

Slash Slash

LOOKS PRETTY GORY.

DEFINITELY. IT'S ONE OF THOSE GAMES WHERE YOU HAVE TO BE FAST OR YOU'RE DEAD.

Slash Whap Slash

WRITING YOUR REPORT? GOOD FOR YOU!

In conclusion,

AND FAST YOU ARE.

WHY, THANK YOU.

Slash whap

AMEND

AND TO THINK I USED TO WONDER IF I WAS UNDERPAID.

I TAKE IT WE WEREN'T SUPPOSED TO SHAKE THE VIAL THAT SAID, "DO NOT SHAKE."

EEGAD! MY PANTS ARE DISSOLVING!

AMEND

MR. FOX, THERE'S A DAN DALTON HERE TO SEE YOU.

YOU'VE GOT TO BE KIDDING ME.

THAT GUY'S THE BIGGEST PAIN IN THE REAR I'VE EVER MET. TELL HIM I'M OUT. TELL HIM I'M IN A MEETING. TELL HIM TO TAKE HIS STUPID SALES PITCH TO WHERE THE SUN DOESN'T SHINE.

AND PLEASE TELL ME YOU'RE USING THE HANDSET AND NOT THE SPEAKERPHONE...

UM...

WHY DON'T I TELL HIM...

AMEND

MOM, WE NEED TO TAKE QUINCY TO THE VET.

WHAT'S WRONG?

I THINK HE'S GONNA BE SICK.

WHAT FROM?

HE CRAWLED INTO THE BATHROOM WHILE PAIGE WAS STEPPING OUT OF THE SHOWER.

IT'S A MIRACLE HE HASN'T THROWN UP ALREADY.

I'M SURE HE'LL LIVE.

BUT WILL HIS **OWNER?**

I'M BEGINNING TO SEE WHY STILTWALKING HASN'T CAUGHT ON AS A CRAZE.

IF ONLY THERE WERE SOME WAY TO DO THIS ON THE MOON.

HI. I'D LIKE A HAPPY McMEAL, A JUNIOR McMEAL AND THREE CHEESY McMEALS.

A HAPPY McMEAL AND TWO TACOS. ANYTHING ELSE?

I DIDN'T SAY TACOS - I SAID A HAPPY McMEAL, A JUNIOR McMEAL AND THREE CHEESY McMEALS.

WHAT KIND OF DRESSING WOULD YOU LIKE ON YOUR SALAD?

I DIDN'T ORDER A SALAD!

WE DON'T MAKE SEAFOOD SALADS.

I COULDA SWORN I DESERVED A BREAK TODAY.

YOUR TOTAL COMES TO $97.17. PLEASE DRIVE THROUGH.

FoxTrot
BILL AMEND

Dear Diary,

It's time I told the truth. It's time I came clean.

I'm really a space alien.

I only pretend to be human. In reality, I am a loathsome, tentacled, squid-like creature.

One look at my true face would kill anyone with eyeballs. I'm that ugly.

I also eat my boogers.

YOUR DIARY'S AWFULLY THIN — HAVE YOU BEEN RIPPING OUT PAGES?

DON'T ASK.

"SLAM!"

PAIGE, WHAT'S WRONG?

OOO, THAT BILLY WEIR— WHO DOES HE THINK HE IS?!

I'VE NEVER FELT SO LOW AND HUMILIATED! SOMEONE NEEDS TO EXPLAIN TO HIM THAT NOT **EVERY** GIRL AT SCHOOL **WANTS** TO BE HIS LITTLE LOVE TOY!

DID HE MAKE INDECENT ADVANCES?

NO. HE RESISTED MINE. LIKE HE COULD DO BETTER!

YOU'LL BE WANTING NEW BOOK COVERS AGAIN, I TAKE IT.

AMEND

LET'S SEE... I NEED A LOAF OF BREAD...

A PACK OF BOLOGNA... A PACK OF SALAMI... TWO PACKS OF CHEESE— ONE AMERICAN, ONE SWISS...

MUSTARD... MAYONNAISE... AND A HEAD OF LETTUCE.

SHOPPING LIST?

PETER'S SANDWICH INSTRUCTIONS.

WE'RE OUT OF CEREAL AGAIN.

AMEND

♪ MACHO, MACHO MAN... I WANT TO BE... ♪ A MACHO MAN...

MACHO, MACHO MAN... ♪ I WANT TO BE... ♪ A MACHO MAN...

AMEND

I WISH I HADN'T TOLD YOU THAT I HATE THAT SONG.

YOU'RE LUCKY WE DON'T KNOW MORE VERSES.

IS IT "MACHO" OR "NACHO"?

HEY, PETER— HOW FAST CAN YOU GO?

JASON, I'M SPEEDING ALREADY.

WE'RE THE ONLY CAR ON THE ROAD! C'MON, OPEN HER UP!

JASON, NO! I'LL GET IN TROUBLE.

WHO'S GONNA FIND OUT?!

HEY, MOM— DID YOU KNOW YOUR CAR CAN GO 90?

REMIND ME TO OPEN **YOU** UP.

ROGER, GO SEE IF THEY HAVE A LIGHTER BALL.

AS MUCH AS I ORDINARILY LOVE PHYSICS...

MOM, CAN I GO OVER TO NICOLE'S HOUSE?

WHEN WILL YOU BE HOME?

LET ME GO ASK.

WILL THIS BE GOING ON ALL DAY?

SHIVER ME TIMBERS, THE SEA HAG'S BACK FER MARR.

ARRGH ARRGH ARRGH...

FoxTrot
BILL AMEND

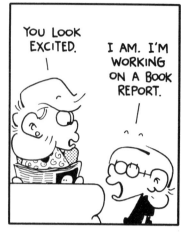

YOU LOOK EXCITED.

I AM. I'M WORKING ON A BOOK REPORT.

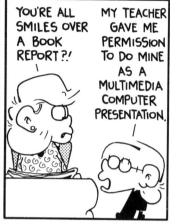

YOU'RE ALL SMILES OVER A BOOK REPORT?!

MY TEACHER GAVE ME PERMISSION TO DO MINE AS A MULTIMEDIA COMPUTER PRESENTATION.

IT'S GOING TO BE THE GREATEST BOOK REPORT EVER. IT'LL HAVE SOUND, ANIMATION, DIGITIZED VIDEO COMMENTARY AND I HAVE AN IDEA FOR A REALLY COOL POINT-AND-CLICK HIERARCHICAL INTERFACE.

SO WHAT'S THE BOOK?

I FORGET. WANNA SEE MY FLOWCHART?

YOU'RE DOING A BOOK REPORT ON "OLD YELLER" AND YOU HAVEN'T EVEN READ IT?!

I'M SURE I'LL GET AROUND TO IT EVENTUALLY.

EVENTUALLY.

RIGHT NOW MY BIGGEST PRIORITY IS GETTING THROUGH ALL THESE COMPUTER MANUALS.

Binary Search Trees in C
J.D. Parker

I WANT MY MULTIMEDIA BOOK REPORT TO BE THE GREATEST AND COOLEST AND MOST AMAZING BOOK REPORT MY SCHOOL HAS EVER WITNESSED.

HAVE YOU EVER BEEN HIT OVER THE HEAD WITH A SUGGESTION?

OLD YELLER

WHAT DO YOU THINK ABOUT USING THE MUSIC FROM "STAR WARS" FOR THE CREDITS?

PHEW.

IT'S TAKEN TWO DAYS OF NON-STOP WORK AND A COUPLE HUNDRED PAGES OF READING...

...BUT I'VE FINALLY DONE IT.

I GOT THE BOOK TITLE TO DANCE ACROSS THE SCREEN.

YOU KNOW, MAYBE THERE'S A REASON MOST KIDS DON'T DO MULTIMEDIA BOOK REPORTS.

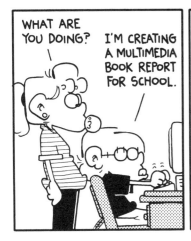

WHAT ARE YOU DOING?

I'M CREATING A MULTIMEDIA BOOK REPORT FOR SCHOOL.

I'VE SPENT ALL WEEK PROGRAMMING THIS THING. IT'S GOT MUSIC... IT'S GOT ANIMATION... IT'S GOT SOUND EFFECTS GALORE... IT'S GOT WIPE EFFECTS THAT'LL KNOCK YOUR SOCKS OFF...

IT'S GOT EVERYTHING.

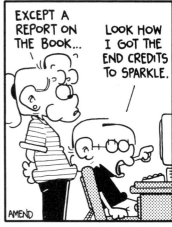

EXCEPT A REPORT ON THE BOOK...

LOOK HOW I GOT THE END CREDITS TO SPARKLE.

THAT CONCLUDES MY INTERACTIVE MULTIMEDIA PRESENTATION ON "OLD YELLER." ANY QUESTIONS?

I HAVE JUST ONE.

ABOUT HOW I GOT THE TEXT TO DANCE ACROSS THE SCREEN? ABOUT THE COMPRESSION ALGORITHM I USED FOR THE SOUND RESOURCE FILES?

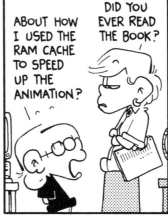

ABOUT HOW I USED THE RAM CACHE TO SPEED UP THE ANIMATION?

DID YOU EVER READ THE BOOK?

I GUESS IF YOU WANT TO GET TECHNICAL...

JASON, SEE ME AFTER CLASS. NEXT UP WILL BE SOPHIA...

HOW'D YOUR BOOK REPORT GO?

LOUSY.

IT SEEMED TOTALLY LOST ON MISS O'MALLEY WHAT A GROUND-BREAKING ACHIEVEMENT MY MULTIMEDIA PRESENTATION REPRESENTED! SHE DIDN'T CARE ABOUT MY ANIMATION... SHE DIDN'T CARE ABOUT MY CLEVER PROGRAMMING TECHNIQUES...

ALL **SHE** CARED ABOUT WAS WHETHER OR NOT I'D ACTUALLY **READ** STUPID "OLD YELLER"!

WHICH, OF COURSE, YOU **HADN'T**.

I MEAN, TALK ABOUT MISSING THE FOREST FOR THE TREES!

FoxTrot
BILL AMEND

DID YOU KNOW THAT THURSDAY IS TAKE YOUR DAUGHTER TO WORK DAY?

YEAH.

YOU SHOULD TAKE PAIGE.

I DON'T KNOW. I WAS THINKING IT MIGHT BE KIND OF EMBARRASSING.

TO HAVE HER AROUND?

TO HAVE HER DISCOVER HOW PATHETIC MY JOB REALLY IS.

GOOD POINT.

YOU COULD DISAGREE A LITTLE...

YO, TOADFACE...

MY NAME IS PAIGE.

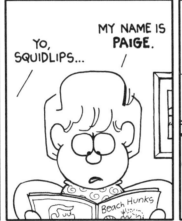

YO, SQUIDLIPS...

MY NAME IS PAIGE.

YO, PAIGE...

MUCH BETTER. NOW WHAT DO YOU WANT?

THWAP!

WHAT HAPPENED TO ALL THE COFFEE I JUST MADE?!

I, UM, DRANK IT.

YOU DRANK A WHOLE POT OF COFFEE?!

WE HAVE A BIG STAFF MEETING THIS MORNING.

THERE'S NOTHING MORE EMBARRASSING THAN FALLING ASLEEP DURING ONE OF PEMBROOK'S ENDLESS SERMONS.

UM, I'LL BE RIGHT BACK...

FOX, THAT'S YOUR FOURTH TRIP TO THE BATHROOM THIS HOUR!

HOW'D YOUR BASEBALL GAME GO?

LOUSY.

I STRUCK OUT TWICE, DROPPED A FLY BALL, MUFFED A GROUNDER AND GOT BEANED IN THE HEAD IN MY FINAL AT-BAT.

AT LEAST YOU GOT ON BASE...

WHEN?

WHEN YOU GOT HIT BY THE BALL.

IT, UM, WAS THROWN FROM MY DUGOUT.

AAAA!

AAAA!

AAAA!

AAAA! AAAA!

MMM... IS THERE ANYTHING BETTER THAN A PACK OF OREOS AFTER DINNER?

...WITH A BIG, TALL GLASS OF WHOLE MILK?

...FOLLOWED BY A HEAPING BOWL OF BEN AND JERRY'S?

MY GUESS WOULD BE YES.

IS THE SCALE SUPPOSED TO SAG LIKE THIS?

FoxTrot
BILL AMEND

WELL, MOM, I FIGURED OUT HOW I'M GONNA MAKE MY MILLIONS.

OH? AND HOW IS THAT?

INVESTING IN COMMODITIES.

COMMODITIES.

I HEARD SOMEONE COULD MAKE, LIKE, A 10,000 PERCENT RETURN IN A YEAR. EVEN IF I DID JUST **HALF** THAT WELL I'D BE A JILLIONAIRE IN NO TIME! IT'S INCREDIBLE! HOW CAN I GO WRONG?!

AMEND

BY THE WAY, WHAT IS A COMMODITY?

JASON, WHEN YOU'RE AT SCHOOL, DO YOU GET A SENSE THAT OTHER KIDS ARE DIFFERENT?

DAD, DO YOU KNOW ANYTHING ABOUT INVESTING IN COMMODITIES?

SORT OF...

THE BASIC IDEA BEHIND COMMODITIES TRADING IS THAT YOU'RE TRYING TO PREDICT WHETHER SOMETHING WILL BECOME MORE SCARCE AND THUS **MORE** VALUABLE, OR LESS SCARCE AND THUS **LESS** VALUABLE.

AMEND

FOR EXAMPLE, IF YOU THOUGHT SPACE ALIENS WERE GOING TO COME AND TAKE AWAY HALF THE WORLD'S COWS, YOU MIGHT WANT TO LOAD UP ON CATTLE FUTURES, SINCE THE LOW SUPPLY WOULD SEND THEIR VALUE THROUGH THE ROOF.

SPACE ALIENS? THIS IS COOLER THAN I THOUGHT.

CONVERSELY, IF YOU KNEW SOMEONE WAS ABOUT TO DISCOVER A GIANT PIRATE CAVE FILLED WITH **GOLD**...

WELL, I'VE GOT MY $5 READY TO INVEST...

AMEND

I'VE GOT THE BASIC PRINCIPLES OF COMMODITY TRADING ALL FIGURED OUT.

NOW ALL I NEED IS A GOOD FINANCIAL ADVISER.

GIVE IT UP, JASON.

AT LEAST LET ME **LOOK** FOR ONE...

I'M **BEING** ONE.

WHAT ARE YOU DOING?

TRYING TO FIGURE OUT WHICH COMMODITY I WANT TO INVEST IN.

THERE ARE JUST SO MANY. THERE'S SOYBEANS... OIL... GOLD... COFFEE... WHEAT... PORK BELLIES...

EEW! DID YOU SAY PORK BELLIES?! GROSS! I'M GONNA THROW UP!

UM, WHY ARE YOU CIRCLING IT?

PAIGE, PASS ME THAT PHONE BOOK, WILL YOU?

MOM, I NEED TO BORROW SOME MONEY.

WHAT FOR?

SO I CAN INVEST IN THE COMMODITIES MARKET AND MAKE MY FORTUNE.

I THOUGHT YOU HAD $5 SAVED UP FOR THAT.

I CALLED A BROKER. THEY REQUIRE $10,000 UP FRONT. WHAT DO YOU SAY?

I HATE THAT LAUGH.

I'LL PAY YOU A DOLLAR TO MOW THE FRONT LAWN...

I HEARD YOU'VE GIVEN UP TRYING TO PLAY THE COMMODITIES MARKET.

NOT ENTIRELY.

WHILE I CAN'T AFFORD TO INVEST WITH A BROKER, I FIGURE I CAN STILL BUY AND SELL COMMODITIES ON MY OWN. ON A MUCH SMALLER SCALE, OF COURSE.

SO WHAT SORT OF COMMODITIES ARE YOU BUYING?

RIGHT NOW I'M RATHER BULLISH ON HO-HOS.

DOES PAIGE KNOW YOU HAVE THESE?

WHY DO YOU THINK I'M BULLISH?

OK, OK, I'LL PAY ANY PRICE...

89

HE HELD MY HAND, NICOLE!

HE HELD MY HANNNND!

DOES HE WANT TO GO TO THE DANCE WITH ME? DOES HE WANT TO ASK ME OUT? WHAT DOES IT **MEAN**?

AMEND

IT MEANS HE HELPED YOU PUT ON A BAND-AID, PAIGE.

I MEANT BESIDES THAT.

TOMMY?...

PAIGE?...

THANKS FOR HELPING ME PUT A BAND-AID ON MY PAPER CUT THIS MORNING.

OH, YOU'RE WELCOME.

AMEND

I'M SORRY IF I SEEMED A LITTLE NERVOUS. IT'S NOT EVERY DAY I HAVE A BOY HOLD MY HAND.

THAT WAS THE FIRST TIME I'D EVER **HELD** A GIRL'S HAND.

YOU KNOW, I, UM, HAVE THIS SPLINTER IN MY PINKIE THAT JUST WON'T-..

BETTER LET ME HAVE A LOOK AT THAT.

MOM! MOM! HE ASKED ME TO THE DANCE!

THE BOY IN YOUR BIOLOGY CLASS?

Newsmonth

YES! TOMMY SMITH! HE WAS SO NERVOUS HE WAS GARBLING ALL HIS WORDS! IT WAS SO CUTE! I COULD BARELY UNDERSTAND A THING HE SAID!

AMEND

Newsmonth

AT LEAST, I **THINK** HE ASKED ME TO THE DANCE.

UM, PAIGE, BEFORE YOU BUY A DRESS...

FoxTrot
BILL AMEND

FoxTrot
BILL AMEND

WHERE ARE MOM AND DAD AGAIN?

AT DAD'S COLLEGE REUNION.

OH, YEAH.

IT'S HIS 25TH.

AMEND

SOUNDS THRILLING.

I THINK DAD JUST WANTED TO GO SEE HOW FAT AND BALD ALL HIS CLASSMATES HAVE GOTTEN.

I WANT TO GO HOME.

TUBBY O'BRIEN— YOU'RE A TWIG! AND THAT HAIR!

CAN YOU BELIEVE IT'S BEEN 25 YEARS?!

NOPE. NOT AT ALL.

I MEAN, IT SEEMS LIKE JUST YESTERDAY WE WERE ALL STANDING HERE AT FRESHMAN ORIENTATION INTRODUCING OURSELVES TO EACH OTHER.

AMEND

YESSIREE...

YUP, YUP...

TED WHITEHEAD.

ROGER FOX.

SO, FRANK...

I'M ROGER.

SO, ROGER... HOW YA BEEN?

GREAT, RICK, AND YOU?

I'M LARRY.

GREAT, LARRY, AND YOU?

AMEND

THIS PLACE SURE BRINGS BACK MEMORIES, ROOMMATES? DOESN'T IT?!

SAY, WEREN'T WE

ROGER FOX? YES...

THE ROGER FOX FROM DELTA THETA HOUSE? YES...

I CAN'T BELIEVE I'VE FINALLY CAUGHT UP WITH YOU AFTER 25 YEARS!...

PIG. UH-OH. ROGER FOX?

EEGAD — IT'S MY OLD GIRLFRIEND, ANNETTE. WHERE?

OVER BY THE BAR. GO SAY HI TO HER.

ARE YOU **INSANE**?! ROGER, IT'S BEEN 25 YEARS. ANDY, THIS WOMAN WAS CRAZY ABOUT ME! I BROKE HER HEART! I SHATTERED HER UNIVERSE! MY SAYING HELLO MIGHT BE VERY, VERY PAINFUL!

ROGER **WHO**? ...VERY, VERY, **VERY** PAINFUL. MORE BEER, MISTER?

WELL, ANDY, I LIVED THROUGH MY COLLEGE REUNION. MMM.

SURE, THERE WERE GUYS WITH MORE HAIR THAN ME... GUYS WITH THINNER WAISTS. CLASSMATES WITH BETTER CAREERS...

BUT I'LL TELL YOU ONE THING — NOBODY HAD A PRETTIER **WIFE** BY HIS SIDE. THANK YOU, ROGER.

...EXCEPT DICK WILSON. WOO! ROGER, WOULD YOU LIKE TO LIVE **BEYOND** YOUR COLLEGE REUNION?..

FoxTrot
BILL AMEND

AAAA!

AAAA!

AAAA!

NEXT ON THE SUMMER ITINERARY...

MAYBE WE SHOULD PACE OURSELVES.

WAY TO GO, PAIGE! YOUR GRADES REALLY IMPROVED!

THANK YOU.

GOOD JOB, PETER! YOU IMPROVED IN EVERY SUBJECT!

THANK YOU.

WELL, JASON, IT LOOKS LIKE YOUR GRADES STAYED THE SAME.

HMMPH.

THE CURSE OF THE A++++ AVERAGE.

OH, WAIT— THEY WENT UP A LITTLE...

WHAT ARE YOU DOING?

TEACHING MYSELF TO WATERCOLOR.

FOOL— WHY DON'T YOU USE THE COMPUTER?

WHAT??

THEY'VE GOT PROGRAMS NOW THAT SIMULATE PAINTS, THAT SIMULATE BRUSHES, THAT SIMULATE PAPER TEXTURES... WHY WOULD YOU WANT TO USE REAL PAINTS WHEN FAKE ONES ARE SO MUCH EASIER?

CAN COMPUTERS DO THIS?..

OK, SHE HAS A POINT.

I THINK I'LL TRY ACRYLICS TOMORROW.

OOO — IS THIS ONE OF THOSE 3-D THINGS?!

MAYBE.

...MAYBE NOT.

I'M NOT GOING TO BED UNTIL I GET THIS...

BOY, DID I HAVE A SCARE THIS MORNING.

OH?

I WAS DRIVING TO WORK WHEN MY CAR STARTED MAKING ALL THESE HORRIBLE SCREECHING AND CLANKING NOISES.

I THOUGHT FOR SURE MY ENGINE WAS COMING LOOSE OR SOMETHING.

SO WHAT WAS IT?

PETER LEFT ONE OF HIS TAPES IN THE STEREO.

I ALWAYS HIT THE EJECT BUTTON BEFORE I GO ANYWHERE.

I WISH I KNEW HOW THE PITCHING WEDGE IS **USED**...

WHAT HAPPENS IF I TRIP GETTING OUT?

Batter's Box

FoxTrot
BILL AMEND

PAIGE, C'MON, WAKE UP! GITCHY GITCHY GOO...

ZZZZ...

DAHN'T BE SILLÉE—MAGIC CARPETS ALWAYS TICKLE YOUR FEET WHEN THEY FLY.

OOO— PIERRE...

PAIGE FOX, WHAT DOES A PERSON HAVE TO **DO** TO WAKE YOU UP?!?

ZZZZ...

BREAKFAST EN BED, MA SWEET?

OOO— PIERRE...

CHOCOLAT
Le Connoisseur Size

PAIGE, I'VE TRIED TO WAKE YOU UP EVERY WAY I KNOW HOW.

ZZZZ...

REASON DIDN'T WORK... FIRMNESS DIDN'T WORK... SCREAMING DIDN'T WORK...

I DON'T KNOW WHAT ELSE I CAN DO!

ZZZZ...

...WHICH IS WHY I'M LETTING JASON TAKE OVER.

I'M UP! I'M UP! I'M UP!

NO FAIR!

HEY, MOM! LOOK WHAT I GOT!

WHAT IS IT?

IT'S A STEALTH BLACKJACK X-220 MODEL ROCKET KIT!

IT TOOK ME 17 WEEKS TO SAVE UP THE MONEY TO BUY IT, BUT IT'S WORTH IT! ISN'T IT GREAT?! ISN'T IT INCREDIBLE?! I CAN'T WAIT TO LAUNCH IT!

WHAT DO YOU SUPPOSE THEY MEAN BY "FAA CLEARANCE REQUIRED"?

JASON, YOU KNOW, THE NEIGHBORS ARE **JUST** STARTING TO SPEAK TO US AGAIN...

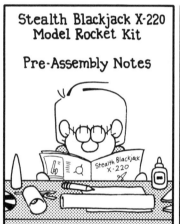
Stealth Blackjack X-220 Model Rocket Kit

Pre-Assembly Notes

In addition to the supplies and materials included with this kit, the following items are recommended for optimal construction and launch of the rocket:

Ruler
White glue
Art knife
Pencil...

..."FIRE EXTINGUISHER"?!.."HIGH-PRESSURE WATER SOURCE"?! "COMPREHENSIVE LIABILITY INSURANCE"?!...

DO WE HAVE THEM OR NOT?

PETER, ARE YOU GONNA BE BUSY LATER TODAY?

WHY?

I THOUGHT MAYBE WE COULD GO FOR A DRIVE.

WHAT FOR?

I'M BUILDING A HIGH-PERFORMANCE MODEL ROCKET AND I WANTED TO DO SOME WIND TUNNEL TESTS BY HOLDING IT OUT THE WINDOW OF A FAST-MOVING CAR.

HOW FAST-MOVING?

WELL, LET'S SEE... IN TERMS OF KILOMETERS PER SECOND...

JASON, DO YOU REMEMBER HOW ANGRY I WAS WHEN YOU **ALMOST** GOT ME ARRESTED?

FoxTrot
BILL AMEND

106

FoxTrot
BILL AMEND

MOM, HAVE YOU SEEN JASON?

HE AND MARCUS JUST RAN OUTSIDE. WHY?

I JUST LOVE SHOPPING AT THIS STORE.

THEY'VE GOT THE BEST STUFF... THE BEST SERVICE...

...THE BEST RETURN POLICY...

I'LL NEED YOUR MOTHER'S CREDIT CARD AGAIN.

GLUG GLUG GLUG

BRAAAP!

"GUT REACTION: A PERFORMANCE PIECE BY JASON FOX." THANK YOU... THANK YOU...

SOME PEOPLE SEEM TO HAVE NO RESPECT FOR THE ARTS.

IS IT JUST ME, OR IS THE TERM "INFORMATION SUPERHIGHWAY" TOTALLY INAPPROPRIATE?

HUH?

I MEAN, SUPERHIGHWAYS WERE A PRODUCT OF THE 1950s AND '60s. THEY REPRESENT THE TRANSPORTATION TECHNOLOGY OF THE PAST.

A HIGH-SPEED DIGITAL COMMUNICATIONS NETWORK DESERVES A MORE FORWARD-LOOKING METAPHOR! ONE THAT CONJURES UP IMAGES OF THE TRANSPORTATION OF **TOMORROW!**

"THE INFORMATION WORM HOLE"...

IS IT JUST ME, OR HAS THIS SUMMER GONE ON TOO LONG ALREADY?

THE RAVEN SINGS AT SUNSET. IN PARIS, THE CAFÉS ARE MANY.

DEEP CAVERNS ARE KNOWN TO ECHO. THE HEAVY FLAG FLAPS NOT AT NIGHT.

ROSES COME IN MANY COLORS. THE LOCAL TRAIN STOPS ON THE HOUR.

THEY'RE ON TO US. OVER AND OUT.

HEY, PAIGE — WANT SOME LEFTOVER STEW? NO.

HOW 'BOUT SOME COTTAGE CHEESE? NO.

SOME RIPE BLACK OLIVES? NO.

JASON, I SAID TO THROW AWAY THE MOLDY FOOD IN THE FRIDGE! I WILL... EVENTUALLY. MOM, I'LL BE AT NICOLE'S.

GOT ANY THREES? NO. GOT ANY FIVES?

NO. GOT ANY SIXES? NO. GOT ANY JACKS?

NO. GOT ANY EIGHTS? NO. GOT ANY TWOS?

GO FISH, YOU MORONS! GO FISH! PAIGE, PLEASE. WE'RE HAPPY PLAYING CARDS. I'LL ASK AGAIN... GOT ANY FIVES?

FoxTrot
BILL AMEND

WHAT A BEAUTIFUL DAY...

...FOR A PHYSICS LESSON.

NOW, PAIGE, AT THIS POINT WE'RE ESSENTIALLY NOTHING BUT POTENTIAL ENERGY, WHICH IS mgh.

Ride the DEATH DEMON 2

AS WE GO DOWN-HILL, THIS IS CONVERTED INTO KINETIC ENERGY, WHICH IS $\frac{1}{2}mv^2$.

SO A QUICK-AND-DIRTY APPROXIMATION OF OUR SPEED AT THE BOTTOM OF A DROP LIKE THIS MIGHT ASSUME $\Delta KE = -\Delta PE$. AND GIVE US $v = \sqrt{2g(-\Delta h)}$.

BUT, IN FACT, OUR CARS ARE CONSTANTLY LOSING ENERGY TO FRICTION. THIS IS WHY THE FIRST HILL HAS TO BE THE HIGHEST.

SEE WHAT I MEAN?

NOW, IN ORDER FOR OUR CAR TO NOT FALL OFF THE TRACK HERE...

JASON, PLEASE, THIS ROLLER COASTER MAKES ME SICK ENOUGH AS IT IS!

AAAA! MY CALCULATOR!

AMEND

FoxTrot
BILL AMEND

FoxTrot
BILL AMEND

WHAT IS IT ABOUT BOYS AND TRAMPOLINES?

OPEN THE WINDOW ON "THREE"...

FoxTrot
BILL AMEND

MOM! MOM! JASON BOUGHT A NEW COMPUTER GAME!

OH?

THE GUY AT THE SOFTWARE STORE SAID IT WAS THE MOST AMAZING GAME HE'S EVER PLAYED! IT'S LIKE TOTALLY ADDICTIVE! NO KID'S EVER BEATEN IT!

IT'S GOT LIKE A MILLION DIFFERENT LEVELS AND WORLDS! IT GOES ON FOREVER! I CAN'T BELIEVE JASON REALLY GOT IT!

SO WHY ARE **YOU** SO EXCITED?

MOM, I'LL BE UP IN MY ROOM UNTIL SEPTEMBER.

THIS GOES WELL BEYOND EXCITEMENT.

AS MUCH AS I ENJOY SEEING THE TWO OF YOU SO HAPPY...

AMEND

JASON, IS IT 8:00 YET?

WHY?

THERE'S A TV SHOW ON THEN THAT I REALLY, REALLY, REALLY WANT TO SEE.

LET'S CHECK. NOPE... IT'S ONLY 7:29.

I BELIEVE YOU MEAN 7:59.

I'VE BEEN KNOWN TO MAKE MISTAKES...

AMEND

WHAT'S FOR DINNER?

I THOUGHT I'D TRY MAKING THAT GARBANZO BEAN CASSEROLE RECIPE I'VE BEEN SAVING.

THE ONE ON THE FRIDGE? THE ONE WITH THE BRAISED TOFU CHUNKS?

THAT'S THE ONE.

YES! YES! YES! YES! YES!

PETER, IT'S NICE TO SEE YOUR TASTES ARE MATURING.

YOU MISUNDERSTAND— DENISE INVITED ME TO EAT OVER AT HER HOUSE.

IN THAT CASE, WHY DON'T I SAVE THAT MEAL FOR TOMORROW.

AMEND

QUINCY, WHAT ARE YOU DOING ON TOP OF PAIGE'S BED?!

YOU KNOW HOW SHE REACTS!... YOU KNOW WHAT SHE'LL DO!...

HOW MANY TIMES DO WE HAVE TO GO THROUGH THIS BEFORE IT SINKS IN?

...PAIGE SCREAMS LOUDER WHEN YOU HIDE UNDER THE SHEETS.

I NEED AN APARTMENT.

. KRNTCH
KRNTCH .
. KRNTCH
KRNTCH .

KRNTCH '
KRNTCH .
KRNTCH .
· KRNTCH

KRNTCH ·
KRNTCH
KRNTCH ·
KRNTCH .

IF IT WAS SUPPOSED TO BE QUIET, THEY'D CALL IT **PRIVATE** CRUNCH.

HAR HAR.

MOM, CAN MARCUS SLEEP OVER TONIGHT?

IT'S OK WITH ME IF IT'S OK WITH YOUR FATHER.

DAD, CAN MARCUS SLEEP OVER TONIGHT?

IT'S OK WITH ME IF IT'S OK WITH YOUR MOTHER.

MARCUS, ARE YOU STILL THERE?...

ANDY, WHAT'S THE MATTER? OH, I GUESS TURNING 42 HAS ME A LITTLE DEPRESSED.

WITH 40 AND 41, I FELT LIKE I WAS JUST A HAIR OUT OF MY 30S. BUT 42 PUTS ME SOLIDLY INTO MY 40S. MIDDLE AGE CENTRAL.

THINK ABOUT IT — I'M PRACTICALLY 45! DO YOU KNOW HOW SCARY THAT IS?!

SEEING AS I'M ABOUT TO TURN 46... OK, BAD EXAMPLE...

ROGER, I WAS THINKING...

I'M 42... YOU'RE 45... PRETTY SOON PETER'LL BE OFF TO COLLEGE... WE'RE BOTH NOT GETTING ANY YOUNGER...

Cartoonist to Judge O.J. Trial

LET'S HAVE ANOTHER KID.

I SHOULD POINT OUT THAT MY **HEART** IS ALSO 45.

THE COUPLE HAD A BABY IN "FOR BETTER OR FOR WORSE"...

ANDY, WHY ON **EARTH** WOULD YOU WANT TO HAVE A BABY?! I DUNNO. I THOUGHT IT MIGHT BE FUN.

"FUN"?! "**FUN**"?! THAT'S WHAT DREAMY-EYED YOUNG COUPLES SAY, NOT 40-SOMETHING MOTHERS WITH THREE HALF-GROWN KIDS! WHAT ARE YOU THINKING?!

...NOT THAT OUR KIDS **AREN'T** LOTS OF FUN.

MOM, JASON BOOBY-TRAPPED THE TOILET AGAIN.

...IT'S JUST THAT THEY'RE **SUFFICIENT** FUN. WE COULD DO IT **RIGHT** THIS TIME...

ANDY, I DON'T MEAN TO BE STUBBORN, BUT WE'VE ALREADY **GOT** THREE KIDS!

I KNOW. YOU'RE RIGHT.

I GUESS I'M JUST A LITTLE PANICKY ABOUT MY AGE. I MEAN, I'M **42**, ROGER! IT'S LIKE MY LIFE IS SLIPPING RIGHT BY! I DON'T **WANT** TO FEEL OLD! I DON'T **WANT** TO FEEL LIKE A HAS-BEEN!

BUT WOULDN'T YOU AGREE THAT HAVING A BABY ISN'T SOMETHING ONE SHOULD DO OUT OF **PANIC**?

MAYBE I'LL JUST GET A FERRARI.

IS THE CRIB STILL UP IN THE ATTIC?

RED... WITH LEATHER...

DAD, WHAT'S WRONG?

AAAA!

IT'S YOUR MOTHER. SHE'S HAVING SOME SORT OF MID-LIFE CRISIS.

FIRST SHE WANTED TO HAVE A BABY, THEN SHE WANTED TO GET A FERRARI, NOW SHE—...

PAIGE AND I ARE OFF TO LOLLAPALOOZA.

IS THIS HER CRISIS OR **YOURS**?

AAAA!

IT'S FUNNY, ROGER.

HERE I WAS ALL WEEK FLIPPING OUT ABOUT MY AGE WHEN ALL I HAD TO DO WAS GO TO A LOLLA-PALOOZA CONCERT WITH PAIGE, AND—

YOU SUDDENLY FELT YOUNG AGAIN?

NO—I WAS THRILLED **NOT** TO BE.

PLEASE CAN I GET A NOSE RING??

SO NO MORE MID-LIFE CRISIS?

I STILL WOULDN'T MIND A FERRARI...

FoxTrot
BILL AMEND

FADE IN:

Opening credits.

Trumpet fanfare.

JASON FOX PRESENTS

FADE TO BLACK.

FADE IN:

EXTERIOR – A&M TOXIC WASTE CO.

Ominous music.

PAN/ZOOM TO:

A drain pipe spewing foul ooze into a nearby marsh.

CUT TO CLOSE-UP:

Bubbles.

Music builds as we see...

...a greenish hand emerge from the vile and disgusting pool of slime!!!

CRANE SHOT:

Out of the goo it rises... a creature born from toxic sludge... a monster whose name would become synonymous with doom!!!

Music crescendos.

Roll title.

THE **PAIGE FOX** STORY

JASON, I'M BUSY. WHY DON'T YOU ASK PAIGE TO PROOFREAD YOUR SCREENPLAY?

UM...